Developing  cy

WORD-LEVEL ACTIVITIES FOR THE LITERACY HOUR

year

Ray Barker

Christine Moorcroft

A & C BLACK

Reprinted 1999 (twice)
First published in 1998 by
A&C Black (Publishers) Limited
35 Bedford Row, London WC1R 4JH

ISBN O-7136-4964-X

The authors and publisher would like to thank the
following teachers for their advice in producing this
series of books: Tracy Adam; Ann Hart; Lydia Hunt; Hazel Jacob;
Madeleine Madden; Helen Mason; Yvonne Newman; Annette Norman;
Katrin Trigg; Judith Wells.

Printed in Great Britain by
St Edmundsbury Press Ltd, Bury St Edmunds, Suffolk.

Contents

Introduction

Developing Literacy supports the teaching of reading and writing by providing a series of activities to develop essential skills in reading and spelling: word recognition and phonics. The activities are designed to be carried out in the time allocated to independent work during the Literacy Hour and therefore should be relatively 'teacher-free'. The focus is on children investigating words and spelling patterns, generating their own words in accordance with what they have learned and, if possible, recognising and devising rules and strategies to enable them to become independent in their recording and further investigation of language.

The activities presented in **Developing Literacy** support the learning objectives of the National Literacy Strategy at word level. Each book
- includes activities which focus on phonics, spelling, word recognition and vocabulary;
- develops children's understanding of sound-spelling relationships;
- helps children to extend their vocabulary by challenging them to talk about and investigate the meanings of words which they find difficult;
- promotes independent work during the Literacy Hour;
- has extension activities on each page which reinforce and develop what the children have learned;
- includes brief notes for teachers at the bottom of most pages.

Some of the activities focus on the high frequency words listed in the National Literacy Strategy's *Framework for Teaching*. These are lists of words to be learned to be recognised on sight. At Key Stage 1, they are words which the children need to know in order to tackle even very simple texts. Some are regular but others, such as 'said' and 'water', do not follow regular phonic spelling patterns. At Key Stage 2, an additional list of medium frequency words is added which children often have difficulty in spelling.

The activities are presented in a way which requires children to read the words rather than just guessing the answers or 'filling in the spaces'. Sometimes they are asked to turn over the sheet and then write a list of words; a partner could read the words aloud for them to write. Working with partners or in groups is encouraged so that children can check one another's reading and co-operate to complete the activities or play games. It is also useful for the children to show their work to the rest of the class and to explain their answers in order to reinforce and develop their own learning and that of others in the class.

Children need to 'Look, Say, Cover, Write and Check' (LSCWCh) words on a regular basis in order to learn their spellings. This has mostly been left to the teacher to initiate. However, it is used on some pages and is presented in the following way in **Developing Literacy**:

- **Look** • **Say** • **Cover** • **Write** • **Check**

Extension

Each activity sheet ends with a challenge (**Now try this!**) which reinforces and extends the children's learning and provides the teacher with an opportunity for assessment. Where children are asked to carry out an activity, the instructions are clear to enable them to work independently, for example,
- List six words and change the vowels.

The teacher may decide to amend this before photocopying, depending on his or her knowledge of the children's abilities and speed of working, for example,
- List **ten** words and change the vowels.

- **Write three questions for your teacher.**
- **Each one should use a different** wh **word.**

Organisation

For many of the activities it will be useful to have a range of dictionaries, fiction and non-fiction books, coloured pencils, counters, scissors and squared paper available and easily accessible. Several activities can be re-used to provide more practice in different letters or sounds, by masking the words and/or letters and replacing them with others of your choice, such as on page 21.

To help teachers to select appropriate learning experiences for their pupils, the activities are grouped into sections within each book. The pages are **not** intended to be presented in the order in which they appear in the books.

The teacher should select the appropriate pages to support the work in progress. Some children may be weak in areas which were covered in previous years. If so teachers can refer to the **Developing Literacy** book for the previous year to find appropriate activity sheets, which may be adapted, to practise those areas. For more able children, the teacher may want to adapt the activity sheets by masking the words and letters and replacing them with more demanding examples.

Many activities will be completed entirely on the activity sheets. On others, particularly in the extension activities, the children will need to work either on the back of the page, on a separate sheet of paper or in an exercise book. Such activities include
- Turn over the page.
- Without copying, write these words (the ones with which they have been working).

or
- Write a new sentence for each word.

It is useful for children to keep their own **word banks** with the new words they have learnt. These could be general or for a specific theme on which the class is working, such as animals. Children should be encouraged to make a note of any words they cannot read so that they can add them to the word bank. The class could also have a **word wall** display to which they can add new words.

Structure of the Literacy Hour

The recommended structure of the Literacy Hour for Key Stage 1 is as follows:

Whole class introduction	15 min	Shared text work (balance of reading and writing) in which the teacher reads or writes a piece of text with the class, to elicit participation in discussion of the topic to be taught.
Whole class activity	15 min	Focused word work in which the children contribute to a teacher-led activity arising from the whole class introduction.
Group work Independent work (rest of class)	20 min	The teacher works with groups of children on guided text work. The other children could work independently, for example, from the **Developing Literacy** activity sheets or on other reading or writing work.
Whole class plenary session	10 min	The teacher leads a review of what has been learned by consolidating teaching points, reviewing, reflecting and sharing the children's ideas and the results of their work.

The following flow chart shows an example of the way in which an activity from this book can be used to achieve the required organisation of the Literacy Hour.

Mary had a little lamb (page 62)

Whole class introduction	15 min

Read aloud the book *Each, Peach, Pear, Plum* by Janet and Allan Ahlberg (Picture Puffin), stopping after the first line on each page, so that the children can supply the missing rhyming character from a nursery rhyme or fairy story, for example,
'Tom Thumb in the cupboard, I spy _____ ' (Mother Hubbard).

Whole class activity	15 min

Give each child a card on which has been written a word (which rhymes with one of these key words: blow, day, rule, tree, man, pot). On the board, draw a large table with a column for each key word. Invite the children to fix their words on to the column with the rhyming key word.

Group work 20 min	Independent work 20 min
Work with one group of children to find words which rhyme.	The others work independently from **Mary had a little lamb** (page 62) from **Developing Literacy Year 2**.

Whole class plenary	10 min

The children share their ideas, adding to the rhyming word chart which was started at the beginning of the lesson.

Teachers' notes

Very brief notes are provided at the end of most pages. They give ideas for maximising the effectiveness of the activity sheets. They may make suggestions for the whole-class introduction, the plenary session or, possibly, follow up work using an adapted version of the activity sheet. Before photocopying, these notes could be masked.

Teachers' note Consider regional accents when doing this work. As a group exercise, children could sort the cards into columns for **ie** and **oa** and **ai** sounds. They could then play snap to reinforce the sounds.

Developing Literacy Year 2
© A & C Black 1998

Using the activity sheets

Brief information is given here about the work within each section of **Developing Literacy Year 2**. Suggestions are also given for additional activities.

Alphabetical order (pages 9-13)

This section revises the learning of the names of the letters and their order in the alphabet and teaches children how alphabetical order can be useful, for example, when using a dictionary or glossary. The activities in this section could be introduced by the use of dictionaries, and glossaries in books from the class or school library.

Alphabet dot-to-dot (page 9) consolidates the children's knowledge of alphabetical order and the names of the letters. Before the activity, the children could sing the alphabet and join in alphabet rhymes. Sources include: *The Oxford Nursery Rhyme Book* by Iona and Peter Opie (Oxford University Press); *The Faber Book of Useful Verse* edited by Simon Brett (Faber); *From Acorn to Zoo* by Satoshi Kitamura (Red Fox); *I Spy: an Alphabet of Art* by Lucy Micklethwait (Collins). The children could also be asked to make up a dot-to-dot puzzle using upper-case letters.

Animal glossary (page 10) introduces the purpose of a glossary, in which alphabetical order helps the user to find a word and its meaning. The children could also look for glossaries in information books and look at how they are organised.

Glossary game (pages 11-12) introduces a glossary which gives more detail about each word, but in which the children can arrange the words in alphabetical order by first letter only. They could play a game in which half the group has the meanings cards and the other half has the glossary words. They have to find their partners.

Dictionary pages (page 10) helps the children to make efficient use of dictionaries. Introduce it by having a group of children at the front of the class holding cards bearing words beginning with the letters **a** to **f**. Arrange them in alphabetical order and ask the rest of the class to explain how you have ordered the group. Mix them up and invite children to put them in order again.

High frequency words (pages 14-29)

This section develops the children's ability to read on sight and spell the high frequency words listed in the National Literacy Strategy's *Framework for Teaching*, which include days of the week and numbers up to twenty.
It also helps the children to build collections of significant words, 'topic-based' words and words of personal interest.

Before they try **Days of the week** (page 14), ask them to say the names of the days of the week. Use a shared text such as *The Very Hungry Caterpillar* by Eric Carle (Picture Puffin) or *Mr Wolf's Week* by Colin Hawkins (Heinemann). This activity reinforces 'Look, Say, Cover, Write, Check' (LSCWCh). It makes use of a verse, to help the children to **remember** the names of the days.

Number words crossword (page 16) helps the children to spell the names of the numbers: if they spell them wrongly, the crossword will not work. Introduce the activity by reading a shared text which includes numbers, such as *Cock-a-Doodle-Do* by Steve Lavis (Ragged Bears), *Ten, Nine, Eight* by Molly Bang (Red Fox), *The Bad Tempered Ladybird* by Eric Carle (Picture Puffin), *The Very Hungry Caterpillar* by Eric Carle (Picture Puffin). They could also make a number line which features the names for the numbers in addition to the numbers themselves.

As soon as I can (page 15) and **Word work 1-8** (pages 17-24) develop the ability to read and spell a collection of high frequency words; grouping the words in a way which makes sense, and reinforces the use of 'Look, say, cover, write, check'. **As soon as I can** (page 15) features words concerning time. The children could begin personal word banks of time words such as now, later, afterwards.

Word work 1 (page 17) introduces the apostrophe which is developed in **Developing Literacy Year 3**. **Word work 2** (page 18) focuses on words which begin with **h**. **Word work 3** (page 19) concentrates on **f**. **Word work 4** (page 20) concentrates on **o**, and includes words in which **o** has different sounds. These different **o** sounds could be a focus for discussion. In **Word work 5** (page 21) all the words contain **x** and in **Word work 6** (page 22) they all begin with **s**.

The use of mnemonics is introduced in **Word work 7** (page 23), to help the children to spell 'their' and 'there' and use them correctly. The children could make their own mnemonics for other words they find difficult to spell.

In **Word work 8** (page 24), the children consolidate their spelling of words beginning with **wh** which are often used in questions. It also introduces the question mark. Introduce the activity with a shared text in which there are questions. Pause after each sentence so that children can say whether or not it is a question.

Word machines (page 25) introduces the prefixes **dis-** and **un-**, showing how they can be used to make opposites. More prefixes are introduced in **Developing Literacy Year 3**. Introduce the activity by reading, with the children, any text to which they can supply opposites, for example, *Do Pigs have stripes?* by Melanie Walsh (Picture Mammoth), *Busy as a Bee* by Sue Heap (Little Hippo), *Cat among the Cabbages* by Alison Bartlett (Levinson).

Insect word bank and **Weather word bank** (pages 26-27) show how topic word banks can be compiled. The children could compile their own word banks about other topics. **My difficult words: Aa to Kk** and **Ll to Mm** (pages 28-29) are an interesting format on which the children can write words where spellings give them trouble. They include high frequency words from the *Framework for Teaching*.

Syllables (pages 30-31)
In this section the children learn to recognise aurally, and count syllables in monosyllabic and multi-syllabic words. In **Say and clap** (page 30), syllables are introduced as 'beats' to which the children can clap. The children listen to the syllables in people's names. They continue to listen and clap to the beat of syllables in **Syllable sacks** (page 31). Introduce these activities by inviting the children to join in well known rhymes while clapping each syllable.

Onset and rime (pages 32-40)
'Onset' means the first sound of a word or syllable and 'rime' means the part which follows. At this stage onset and rime in entire words only are considered. The section begins with **Tongue-twister** (page 32), which focuses on only the first sound of each word. The children learn to distinguish between the first sound of a word and the rest of the word, to identify the sound and to write it. This section also develops the children's ability to discriminate between, read and spell the long vowel phonemes, for example, **oa, ai, ea**, and **or**.

Onset and rime chart (page 33) and **Onset and rime dice** (page 34) provide collections of onsets and rimes which can be combined to make short monosyllabic words. They also introduce the use of charts for recording. Before using **Onset and rime dice** (page 34) cover **sh, ch** and **th** (pages 35-38). The activity encourages spelling by analogy, by asking the children to make up words using the onsets with other rimes. They develop their ability to blend phonemes when reading. Introduce the activities by writing on a large sheet of paper an onset, such as **b** and asking the children to suggest a word.

Phonemes (pages 35-46)
The activities on pages 35-40 all concentrate on phonemes which are made from 2 letters (digraphs). **Shelly's shop** (page 34) is based on words beginning with '**sh**', while **Charlie's chest** (page 35) is based on '**ch**', and **The match** (page 37) is based on '**sh** and **ch**'. After the activities, the children could play a guessing game: 'I'm thinking of a **sh** which sails on water' (ship), 'I'm thinking of a **ch** which is a fruit,' (cherry), and so on.

A phoneme is the smallest unit of sound in a word. The activities help the children to discriminate between the phonemes in a word, and reinforce their knowledge of the terms 'vowel' and 'consonant'. In **Phoneme fish** (page 41), the initial and final phoneme of each word are provided and the children are asked to find the middle (long vowel) phoneme. Introduce the activity by giving a group of six children words whose vowels are missing. Give another six children the missing vowels. Ask them to find their partners. If any children are left without partners with whom they can make real words, can they find anyone with whom to swap places?

ea words (page 42) develops grapheme/phoneme correspondence. A grapheme is a letter or group of letters used to spell a phoneme; the same grapheme can produce different phonemes and the same phoneme can be represented by different graphemes, for example, **ea** in 'leaf' is a different phoneme to **ea** in 'bread'. The children are asked to listen to the middle phoneme of each word (**ea**) and to decide whether it sounds like '**ea**' in 'bread' or '**ea**' in 'leaf'. They learn that the combination of the same two letters can have different sounds. In **Phoneme snap 1** and **2** (pages 44-45) they also learn that a phoneme can be spelt in different ways.

Lost vowels (page 45) consolidates the children's knowledge of vowels. Introduce the activity using simple CVC words with their vowels missing, such as cat, dog, bat, pin and rat, which can be accompanied by pictures. The children can supply the missing vowels. After the activity, the children could have fun changing some of the vowels in a given sentence to make a silly sentence, for example, 'The cat was on the bed' might become 'The cut was in the bud.'

Making new words (page 46) provides an opportunity for the children to spell words by analogy. They are provided with a word and asked to make a new word by adding one letter which does not change the sounds of the vowel.

Word-building (pages 47-54)

This section is mainly about spelling by analogy; the children combine phonemes they know to make new words. This develops confidence in spelling (If you can spell 'ink', you can spell 'drink'). The section is divided into activities which focus on particular word-endings and -beginnings and the effects of adding and taking away letters. As in **Lost vowels** (page 45), they can have fun turning a given sentence into a silly sentence, by deleting letters, for example, 'They flew to Spain in a plane' might become 'The few to spin in a lane', and 'These plants grow on rocks' might become 'These pants row on rocks'.

In **Subtraction word puzzles** (page 51), the children investigate the effects of removing a letter from a word. They should notice any changes in vowel sounds, as in **wine/win**. As in **Lost vowels** (page 45), they can have fun turning a given sentence into a silly sentence by deleting letters.

Word dominoes (page 52) encourages the children to read and spell by analogy. To avoid confusion, the graphemes used always represent the same phonemes. An extension could be to replace the beginnings and endings with others which might produce words in which the same grapheme produces different phonemes, for example, dead, bread, dear, lead, your, four, sour, flour. This activity, as well as **Word chain** (page 53) and **Word link** (page 54), encourages the children to segment words to aid their reading and spelling.

Word endings (pages 55-59)

This section develops the children's ability to read and spell root words and the resulting words when endings are added to them. It includes specific endings which the National Literacy Strategy's *Framework for Teaching* suggests for Year 2: **ed**, **ing**, **ful** and adding **s** and **es** to form plurals. At this stage the endings do not change the rest of the root word. In **Developing Literacy Year 3**, words are used where the root word is changed when the ending is added, for example, when **e** is lost or a final consonant is doubled. Children who are ready for work at that level could tackle the activities in **Developing Literacy Year 3**.

Names (pages 60-61)

This section provides puzzles which the children can develop to include their own names and those of their friends and family. **Name puzzles** (page 60) also provides practice in recognition of initial consonant phonemes. Introduce the activity by showing the children three objects whose initials spell a word. What are the letters? What is the word? Examples could be a pencil, an orange and a tea bag for the word pot and a glove, an apple, a tie and an egg for the word gate. **Words from names** (page 61) develops spelling skills as the children use the letters of their own and other names to make words. It also introduces, at a simple level, the idea of anagrams and part-anagrams, which are featured in later books. Some children might need to use plastic or wooden letters during the extension activity. During the plenary session, invite them to display all the words they can make from their own and other children's names.

Rhymes (pages 62-64)

This section develops identification, spelling and reading of phonemes.

Glossary of terms used

analogy Recognising a word, phoneme or pattern in known words and applying this to new, unfamiliar words.
blending Running together individual phonemes in pronunciation.
cluster A combination of consonant sounds before or after a vowel (or 'y' used as a vowel); for example, **spr**ay, **cr**y.
digraph A combination of two letters which represents one phoneme; for example, **ch**ips, **th**e, fi**sh**, **ch**erry.
grapheme A letter or letters used to represent a phoneme.
mnemonic A device to aid memory; for example, 'i before e except after c'.
onset The initial consonant or consonant cluster of a word or syllable; for example, **tr**ain, **scr**ape, **sk**ate.
phoneme The smallest unit of sound in a word. A phoneme can be represented by one or more letters; for example, st**ay**, s**igh**t, st**ee**p.
phonics The relationship between sounds and the written form of a language.
prefix An affix at the beginning of a word which changes the word's meaning; for example, **un**do, **re**play, **over**come.
rhyme The use of words which have the same sound in their final syllable; for example, fox/rocks, sore/door.
rime The part of a word or syllable which contains the vowel and final consonant or consonant cluster; for example, sh**eep**, sl**ow**, f**oal**.
suffix An affix at the end of a root word; for example, sing**ing**, slow**ly**.
syllable A rhythmic segment of a word; for example, can (1 syllable), car- ton (2 syllables), can- op- y (3 syllables), tel- e- vis- ion (4 syllables).

Alphabet dot-to-dot

- **Join the dots from a to z.**

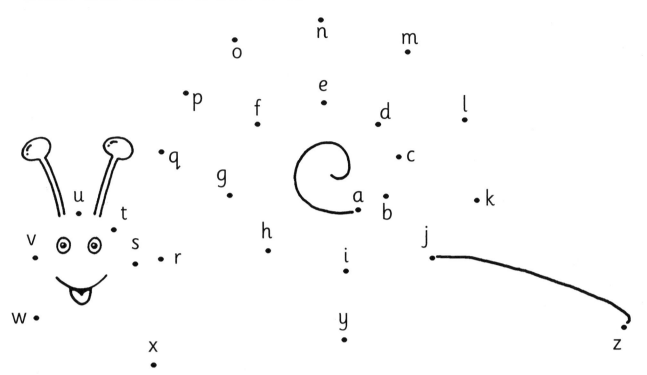

- **What have you drawn?** _____

- **Make your own puzzle by writing the letters c to z by the dots.**

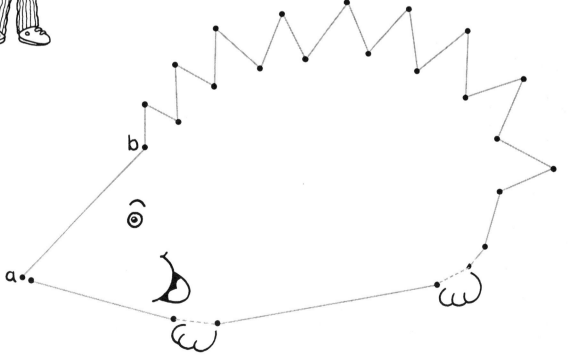

Teachers' note Ask the children to read the alphabet on each puzzle.

Developing Literacy Year 2
© A & C Black 1998

Dictionary pages

• **Write these words on the correct dictionary page.**

~~car~~	gold	by	dog	leaf	fish	vet
tree	hip	zip	on	park	star	rose
me	ant	jet	uncle	egg	net	queen
web	ink	key				

Dictionary pages

Aa	Bb	Cc Car	Dd	Ee	Ff
Gg	Hh	Ii	Jj	Kk	Ll
Mm	Nn	Oo	Pp	Qq	Rr
Ss	Tt	Uu	Vv	Ww	Xx Yy Zz

Now try this!

• **Think of other words.**

Write them on the dictionary pages.

Teachers' note After completing this activity, some children might be able to locate these words in a dictionary and write the meanings of the words they find.

Developing Literacy Year 2
© A & C Black 1998

• **Match the meanings to the words.**

calf	a pig's nose
cub	a young horse
foal	a young pig
hoof	a horse's foot
kitten	a young lion
lamb	a young cow
paw	a young cat
piglet	a cat's foot
puppy	a young sheep
snout	a young dog

Now try this!

• **With friends, make a glossary for clothes.
These words may be useful.**

trousers   shirt   vest

Teachers' note The children could collaborate in writing glossaries with meanings in which they use lists of words which they are given (in alphabetical order), before progressing to compiling glossaries about given subjects, such as families, birds and dinosaurs.

Developing Literacy Year 2
© A & C Black 1998

Glossary game cards

Glossary word cards

a aeroplane	**b** bike	**c** coach
e estate car	**h** helicopter	**j** jeep
l lorry	**m** minibus	**p** pram
s submarine	**t** train	**y** yacht

Meaning cards

It has wings and travels in the air.	It has two wheels. You pedal it.	It has seats for about forty people. It travels on roads.
It is a long car with a big space for luggage.	It has rotors and travels in the air.	It has four wheels and can travel on rough ground.
It travels on roads. It carries big loads.	It is a small bus or coach.	A baby travels in it.
It travels under the sea.	It travels on a railway.	It is a boat with sails.

Teachers' note Use a different colour for each set of cards. The instructions for this game are on page 13.

Developing Literacy Year 2
© A & C Black 1998

Glossary game

- **Play with a partner.**
- **Sort the cards into glossary words and meanings.**

glossary words   meanings

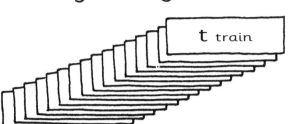 

t train

A baby travels in it.

- **Spread them face down**

glossary words   meanings

- **Take turns to turn over a glossary word card and a meaning card.**
- **If they match keep the pair of cards.**

a aeroplane

It has wings and travels in the air.

- **If not, turn them face down with the other cards.**
- **The winner is the one with the most pairs of cards when all the cards have been turned over.**

Now try this!

- **Put the glossary words in alphabetical order.**
- **Match them with their meanings.**

Teachers' note *The glossary cards are on page 12.*

Days of the week

Look • Say • Cover	• Write	✓ or ✗ • Check
Monday		
Tuesday	_____	
Wednesday	_____	
Thursday	_____	
Friday	_____	
Saturday	_____	
Sunday	_____	

Monday _____   Monday

• **Complete the days of the week.**

Solomon Grundy

Born on M _ _ day

Christened on T _ _ _ day

Married on W _ _ _ _ _ day

Took ill on Th _ _ _ _ _ _ _

Worse on F _ _ _ _ _ _

Died on S _ _ _ _ _ _ _ _

Buried on S _ _ _ _ _ _

That was the end of Solomon Grundy.

Now try this!

• **With a partner, make up a happy verse about Solomon Grundy.**

• **Write it and tape record it.**

Teachers' note For more practice in the spellings of the days of the week, the children could collaborate in groups to make pictorial timetables for the class, with different children drawing and labelling pictures of regular weekly activities.

Developing Literacy Year 2
© A & C Black 1998

- Write |soon| or |as| in the spaces.

- **Read the sentences.**
  Check that they make sense.

How **soon** can we go to the fair?

_As_ _soon_ _as_ _____
I have cut the grass.

_____ _____ _____ it is dark, switch on the light.

It will _____ be spring.

The box is _____ light _____ a feather.

_____ I was passing the house a dog ran out.

Come and see me _____ .

Now try this!

- **Write four of your own sentences using**
  |soon| **and** |as|.

Teachers' note Ask the children to look in books and other texts for words which end like **soon** or which have **as** in them.

Developing Literacy Year 2
© A & C Black 1998

Number words crossword

Across		Down	
1.	13	**2.**	11
4.	15	**3.**	19
5.	2	**4.**	4
6.	20	**5.**	3
7.	10	**6.**	12
9.	1	**8.**	1
10.	7	**9.**	1

• Write the names of the numbers between one and twenty which are not on the crossword grid.

Teachers' note Do the children know the meanings of **across** and **down**? They might also need to be shown the conventions of crossword numbering and shown, for example, why there are no clues for 2 or 3 across.

Developing Literacy Year 2
© A & C Black 1998

Word work 1

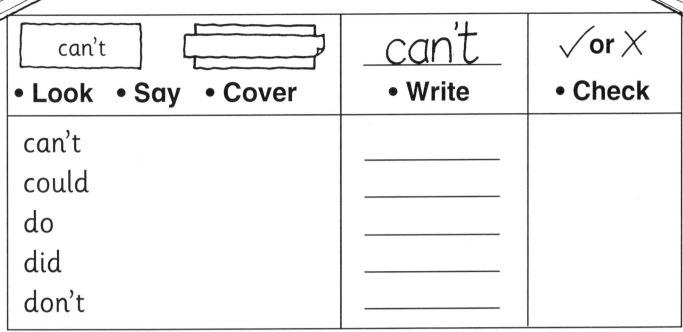

can't			can't	✓ or ✗
• Look • Say • Cover			• Write	• Check
can't could do did don't			_____ _____ _____ _____ _____	

• Circle these words in the word search.

can't   did
could   don't
do

s	o	l	l	c	a	n	t
d	u	d	a	i	d	t	d
a	a	o	c	a	t	u	o
d	b	n	t	d	a	t	o
i	o	t	a	c	o	l	t
d	d	d	c	o	u	l	d

• Write these words on the grid.

can't   did
could don't
do

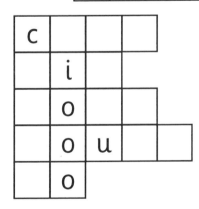

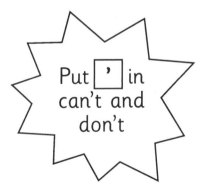

Put ' in can't and don't

Now try this!

• Look in books for words with ' **like** can't **and** don't .

• Write the words you have found.

• Why do they have ' **?**

Teachers' note Talk about the meanings of **can't** and **don't**. The children could write **can't** and **don't**, and any other contractions they find, in full.

Developing Literacy Year 2
© A & C Black 1998

Word work 2

- **Look for words which begin with** `h`.
- **Write them on the notepad.**

`h` **words**

her

- **Colour the shapes in which there are** `h` **words.**

her
car
half
crab
had
his
or
have
save
home
house
cow
me

how
so
eat
it
try
go
has
hair
old
it
him

- **Write the** `h` **words which rhyme with these.**

bad ————   fare ————

calf ————   rim ————

jazz ————   fizz ————   fur ————

roam ————   mouse ————   cow ————

- **Add some more** `h` **words to the notepad.**

Teachers' note Encourage the children to say the words. This will help to recognise words which rhyme but are not spelt the same, for example, **home** and **roam**.

Developing Literacy Year 2
© A & C Black 1998

Word work 3

- **Read the words in the box.**

if	of	off	after	first

- **Which letter is in all these words?** ___

- **Look in books to find words which have** f .

- **Write them on the correct notepad.**

Words beginning with f	Words with ff	Other f words
first fire	off snuffle	if after

 **• Circle the** f **which sounds like** v .

if	of	off	after	first

- **Write a sentence each for** of **and** off .

Teachers' note The children could make up tongue-twisters or sentences with **f** sounds. They could recite these to the rest of the class during the plenary session. In future lessons, an adult could help them to write their tongue-twisters, which the children could then illustrate.

Developing Literacy Year 2
© A & C Black 1998

Word work 4

- **Read the words in the box.**

old	once	or	our	out	over	one

- **Find rhyming partners from the box.**

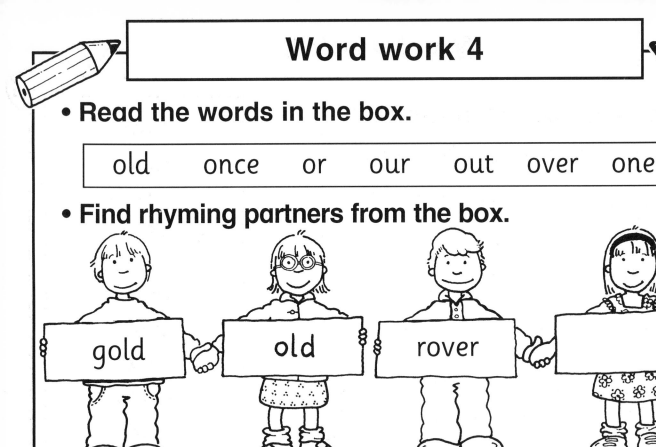

gold   old   rover

for   tower

shout

- **On the notepad write five other words beginning with** o .

Teachers' note Ask the children to look in books they know, to find words beginning with 'o' and to read them aloud. Discuss with the children the sounds which 'o' can make.

Developing Literacy Year 2
© A & C Black 1998

20

Word work 5

- **Read the words in the box.**
- **Copy them on to the flags.**

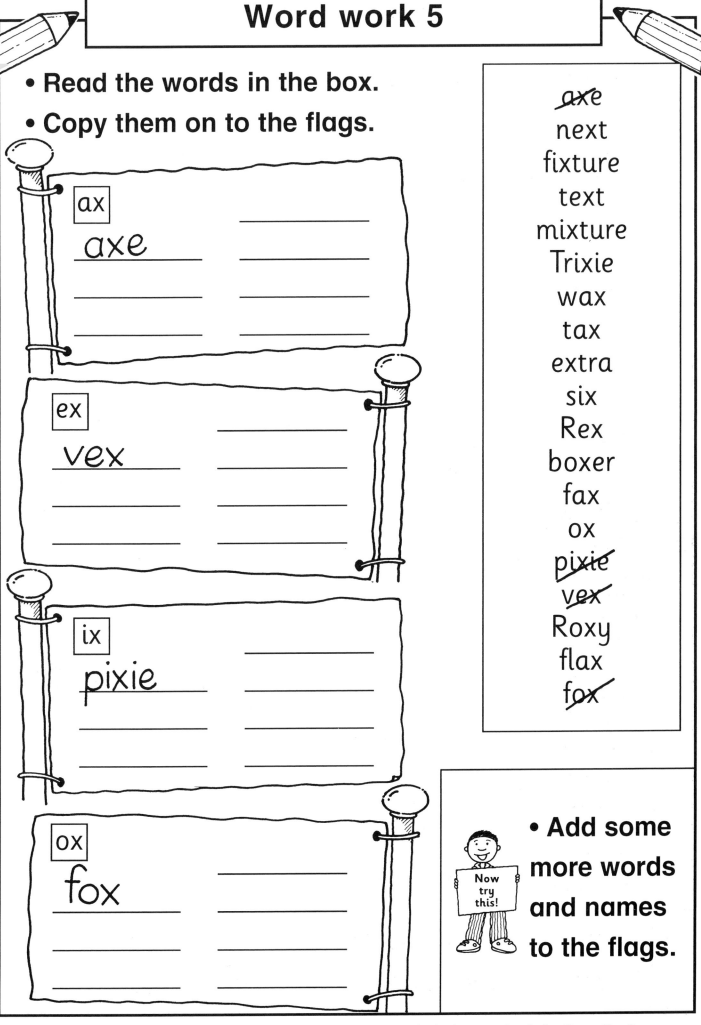

ax
axe

ex
vex

ix
pixie

ox
fox

axe
next
fixture
text
mixture
Trixie
wax
tax
extra
six
Rex
boxer
fax
ox
pixie
vex
Roxy
flax
fox

Now try this!

- **Add some more words and names to the flags.**

Teachers' note The children could look for brand names and the names of people and animals.

Word work 6

- **Read the tongue-twister.**
- **Underline all the words which begin with** ⬚ s .

Sarah's sister saw some sausages.
She should have seen a sign saying school.

- **Write the** ⬚ s **words from the tongue-twister which rhyme with these words.**

paw _____   fool _____
bean _____   could _____
mister _____   come _____

- **Write the** ⬚ s **words from the tongue-twister which begin in the same way as these words.**

⬚sch olar _____   ⬚see k _____
⬚sh eet _____   ⬚sh ow _____

- **Write a sentence using** ⬚so **and** ⬚some .

Teachers' note Encourage children to read the words aloud. They should notice different ways to spell the same sound.

Developing Literacy Year 2
© A & C Black 1998

Word work 7

A mnemonic helps you remember. Here are two mnemonics to help you remember there and their.

T h e i r
h o u s e
e n d s
i t s
r o w .

Over here or over t here

'Here' is in there !

• **Write** their **or** there **in the spaces.**

They wore _____ coats.

_____ are the children.

They are with _____ mum.

They are carrying _____ shoes.

_____ dog is running in front of them.

Where is _____ grandmother?

_____ is Simon.

She is over _____ .

Now try this!

• **Copy the two mnemonics in colourful writing or print them using a colour printer.**

• **Check your last story for mistakes using** their **and** there **. Correct the mistakes.**

Teachers' note Explain **mnemonic** and let the children practise saying it. They might notice that the initial **m** is silent. Give them an example of other mnemonics, for example, for remembering the colours of the rainbow (**R**ichard **o**f **Y**ork **g**ave **b**attle **i**n **v**ain).

Developing Literacy Year 2
© A & C Black 1998

Word work 8

Who? Why? What? Which? When? Where?

• **Write a different one of these words in each space.**

| who | why | what | when | where | which |

_____ is Megan wearing gloves on her feet?

_____ is she coming home?

_____ dog belongs to Megan?

_____ knows where Megan is?

_____ was she going?

_____ is my name?

Now try this!

• **Write three questions for your teacher.**
• **Each one should use a different** wh **word.**

Teachers' note After this activity, ask the children to look in books for a question word which does not begin **wh** (how). They could ask and write some **how** questions.

Developing Literacy Year 2
© A & C Black 1998

Word machines

- **Make the words into their opposites**
  by adding dis **or** un .

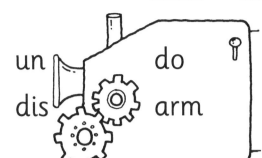

un | do — undo
dis | arm — disarm

- **Write the words on the notepad.**

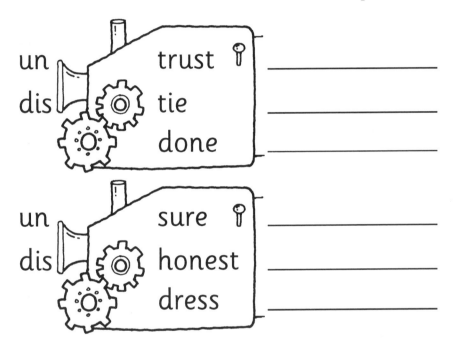

un / dis | trust _____
tie _____
done _____

un / dis | sure _____
honest _____
dress _____

- **Look in a dictionary for the meanings of the words you have made.**

 Now try this!

- **List other words which start with** un **or** dis .

_____ _____ _____

_____ _____ _____

Teachers' note The children could make up some **silly** opposites using **un-** and **dis-**, explaining their meanings, for example, unwrite (erase), unfix (damage or break).

Developing Literacy Year 2
© A & C Black 1998

Insect word bank

• **Complete the insect names.**

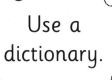
Use a dictionary.

a _ _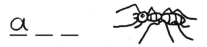

e a r _ _ _

b _ _

f _ _

butter _ _ _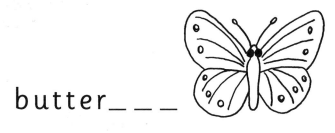

_ _ _ _ _ _ _ _

cr _ cket

mosq _ _ _ _

dr _ _ _ nfly

cr _ n _ fl _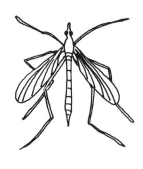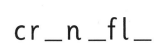

Now try this!

• **List some more insects.**
• **Use a dictionary or a book about insects.**

Teachers' note Ask the children to LSCWCh the insect names.

Developing Literacy Year 2
© A & C Black 1998

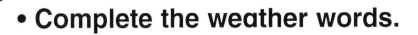

• **Complete the weather words.**

baro **meter**

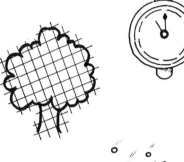

_ _ _ _ _

f _ g

fr _ _ _

h _ _ _ stones

hurr _ _ _ _ _

_ _ _ _ _ _ _ _ _

_ _ icle

_ _ _ _ _ _ _

r _ _ _

_ _ _

_ _ _ _ _

• **Write three more weather words in sentences.**
• **Use a dictionary or a book about weather.**

Now try this!

Teachers' note Ask the children to LSCWCh the weather words.

Developing Literacy Year 2
© A & C Black 1998

27

My difficult words: Aa to Kk

Aa
about

Bb
because

Cc
could

Dd
don't

Ee
elephant

Ff
first

Gg
going

Hh
half

Ii
island

Jj
jump

Kk
key

Teachers' note The children should keep these pages and add any other difficult words they come across.

Developing Literacy Year 2
© A & C Black 1998

Ll
laugh

Mn
many

Nn
night

Oo
once

Pp
people

Qq
quiz

Rr
rough

Ss
should

Tt
these

Uu
umbrella

Vv
very

Ww
water

Xx
x-ray

Yy
yacht

Zz
zero

Teachers' note The children should keep these pages and add any other difficult words they come across.

Developing Literacy Year 2
© A & C Black 1998

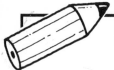

Say and clap

- **Say the names.**
- **Clap each syllable.**
- **Write the number of syllables.**

Robert | Ro | bert | - 2

Fiona | Fi | o | na | - 3

John

Angela

Rani

Ahmed

___

Jan

James

Benjamin

Hannah

___   ___   ___   ___

- **Say and clap the names of your group.**
- **Count the syllables.**

Teachers' note The children could take turns to say a name for a partner to clap the syllables.

Developing Literacy Year 2
© A & C Black 1998

Syllable sacks

- **Say and clap the names of the fruits.**
- **Write them in the correct syllable sacks.**

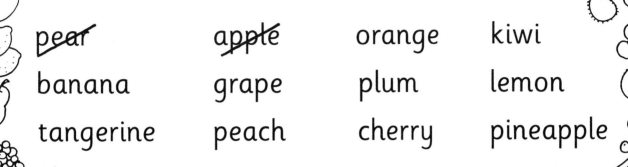

pear	apple	orange	kiwi
banana	grape	plum	lemon
tangerine	peach	cherry	pineapple

1 syllable	2 syllables	3 syllables
pear	apple	

- **Add some vegetables to each sack.**

Now try this!

- **Clap the names of things in the classroom.**
- **Write them on cards.**
- **Sort them into these sets.**

| 1 syllable | 2 syllables | 3 syllables or more |

Teachers' note During the plenary session, the children could take turns to say the name of a food for others to clap and count its syllables.

Developing Literacy Year 2
© A & C Black 1998

- **Read aloud these tongue-twisters.**

- **Underline the beginning sound of each word.**

Robert Rowley rolled a round roll round,
A round roll Robert Rowley rolled round.
Where rolled the round roll
Robert Rowley rolled round?

- **Which sound is at the beginning of most of the words?** ___

Betty Botter bought some butter,
But, she said, the butter's bitter.
If I put it in my batter
It will make my batter bitter,
But a bit of better butter
Would make my batter better.

- **Which sound is at the beginning of most of the words?** ___

Now try this!

- **Make up a silly sentence with lots of words beginning with** ⬚c⬚ **. These words may help.**

  clever   crab   can't

- **Make up a silly sentence with lots of words beginning with** ⬚t⬚ **. These words may help.**

  tell   Tom   tiger

Teachers' note During the whole class introduction, read the class several tongue-twisters. Ask if the children know any more.

Developing Literacy Year 2
© A & C Black 1998

Onset and rime chart

- **Make a word from each onset and rime.**
- **Write it on the chart.**
- **If it is not a real word, cross it out.**

Check the words in a dictionary.

onset	rime				
	ad	ap	ot	op	up
b	bad	bap	~~bot~~		
c					
d					
h					
l					
m					
p					

Now try this!

- **In the spaces write three different onsets.**
  Finish the chart.

Teachers' note For more practice, mask the rimes and replace them with others of your own choice.

Developing Literacy Year 2
© A & C Black 1998

Onset and rime dice

- **Play the game with a partner.**

You need a set of onset and rime dice.

chip

ch	sh	th
chip	~~shan~~	

- **Roll the dice**
- **List the words you have made.**
- **Cross out any which are not real words.**

Name			Name		
ch	sh	th	ch	sh	th
t	s	f	t	s	f

Teachers' note The dice can be made by writing the onsets (**ch, sh, th, t, s, f**) and rimes (**ip, an, in, at, ap, op**) on pieces cut from adhesive labels and sticking them on to plastic or wooden blocks, or on to large dice. Introduce the terms **onset** and **rime** (see **Introduction**).

Developing Literacy Year 2
© A & C Black 1998

Shelly's shop

- **Colour red everything which begins with** sh **.**

- **List all the things which begin with** sh **.**

_____

_____

Now try this!

- **Look in a dictionary for other** sh **words.**

List five of them.

Teachers' note Some children might be able to suggest or find, in books they know, words which end with **sh** or which have **sh** in the middle.

Developing Literacy Year 2
© A & C Black 1998

- **Colour blue everything which begins with** ch .

- **List all the things which begin with** ch .

_____

_____

- **Read the sentences.**
- **Complete the words.**

I like fish and ch _ _ _.

I can play ch _ _ _.

I sit on a ch _ _ _.

Teachers' note Some children might be able to suggest or find, in books they know, words which end with **ch** or which have **ch** in the middle.

Developing Literacy Year 2
© A & C Black 1998

36

th

- **Read the words.**
- **Underline** th .

the   this   that   these   them

- **Complete the words.**

| | | e | | | | a | t | | | | e | m |

| | | i | s | | | | e | s | e |

- **Find the words in the wordsearch.**
- **Colour them yellow.**

t	h	e	s	e	h	t
h	e	a	n	s	c	o
a	t	k	t	h	e	m
t	h	i	s	a	m	k
a	e	n	c	t	n	k

the
this
that
these
them

Now try this!

- **Look in dictionary for other** th **words.**
- **Write a sentence for each** th **word.**

Teachers' note Some children might be able to suggest or find, in books they know, words which end with **th** or which have **th** in the middle.

Developing Literacy Year 2
© A & C Black 1998

The match

- Read the names in the box.
- Listen for $\boxed{ch}$ or $\boxed{sh}$ at the beginning.
- Write them in the $\boxed{ch}$ or $\boxed{sh}$ team.

Cherry   Shane   Chip   Shazia
Shamus   Chuck   Charlie
Sheila   Shelly   Charity

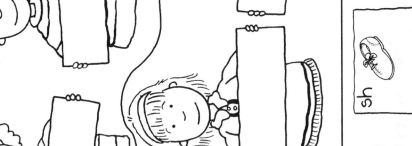

- Cut out and collect pictures to
  make a $\boxed{ch}$ page and $\boxed{sh}$ page.

sh

ch

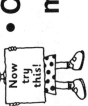

Now try this!

Developing Literacy Year 2

When ph says f

- **Complete the children's names with** ph .
- **With a partner, read the names.**

Ste _ _ anie

So _ _ ie

Ste _ _ an

_ _ ilippa

Ral _ _ _

Jose _ _ _

Del _ _ ine

_ _ ilip

- **Read the words on the notepad.**
- **Write the correct word for each meaning.**

a sea-mammal _____

a chart _____

a picture _____

a greenfly _____

an Egyptian ruler _____

letters in order _____

a prize _____

your brother's or
sister's son _____

graph
dolphin
aphid
nephew
trophy
pharaoh
photograph
alphabet

Now try this!

- **Use a dictionary to find words which begin with** photo . **List them.**

Developing Literacy Year 2
© A & C Black 1998

When ch says k

- **Complete the children's names with** ch **or** Ch **.**
- **With a partner read the names.**

Mi _ _ _ ael

_ _ _ loe

Ni _ _ _ olas

Eno _ _ _

_ _ _ ristopher

_ _ _ ristine

_ _ _ ristian

- **Read the words on the notepad.**
- **Write the correct word for each meaning.**

pain _____

a group of singers _____

tummy _____

a name for Jesus _____

a king or queen _____

where you learn _____

a sound which
bounces back _____

something used
on a ship _____

ache
anchor
choir
Christ
echo
monarch
school
stomach

Now try this!

- **Find the meanings of these words.**

orchid   chemist   chorus

Teachers' note Some children might be able to think of names in which **ch** says **sh**, for example, Cherie, Charlotte. A dictionary of first names might help.

Developing Literacy Year 2
© A & C Black 1998

Phoneme fish

- **Help the cats to make words.**
- **Draw lines to join them to the letters they need.**
- **Read the words.**
- **Write the words.**

d _ _ n

t _ _ k

b _ _ _

g o o d

c _ _ t

b _ _ n

t _ _

oo

ar

oy

ow

g _ _ n

f _ _ m

p _ _ t

cl _ _ n

c _ _ k

cr _ _ n

- **Write other words using these sounds.**

 Now try this!

| oo | oy | ar | ow |

Teachers' note To provide practice with other letter combinations, mask the letters and replace them with others of your choice, for example, **ai**, **ea**, **ou**, **aw**.

Developing Literacy Year 2
© A & C Black 1998

- **Read the words aloud with a partner.**
- **If the ea sounds like br ea d, write the words on the bread.**
- **If the ea sounds like l ea f, write the word on the leaf.**

> ea in bread says '**e**'.
> ea in leaf says '**ee**'.

bean	dear	seat	ready	head
dead	steady	team	tread	lean

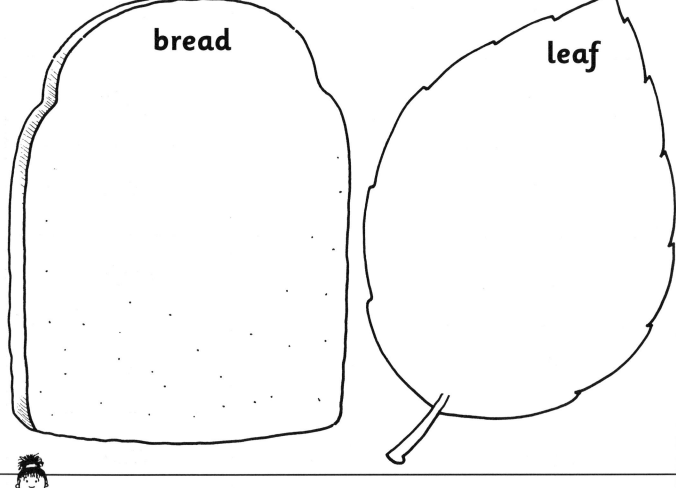

bread

leaf

- **List six more ea words on the bread and the leaf.**

Now try this!

Teachers' note Ask the children to read aloud all the words they have written on the bread and on the leaf. Are they in the correct sets? Some children may spot that the words **read** and **lead** can be pronounced both ways.

Developing Literacy Year 2
© A & C Black 1998

Phoneme snap game 1

- Take turns to put a card on the table face up and say the word.

- If two cards with the same middle phoneme are put down, one after the other, call 'Snap'. The player who says 'Snap' first wins all the cards.

mice	boat	cane
pie	soak	raid
ride	rope	gale
kite	pole	late
lie	coat	main
bike	bowl	tail
mile	toad	rain
tie	hole	mate

Teachers' note As a group exercise, children could sort the cards into columns for **ie**, **oa** and **ai** sounds. They could then play snap to reinforce the sounds. You may need to consider regional accents when doing this work.

Developing Literacy Year 2
© A & C Black 1998

Phoneme snap game 2

- **Take turns to put a card on the table face up and say the word.**
- **If two cards with the same middle phoneme are put down, one after the other, call 'Snap'. The player who says 'Snap' first wins all the cards.**

peel	rule	turn
meal	moon	burn
feel	boot	bird
seen	loop	dirt
seat	fool	girl
bean	June	fur
deep	soon	fern
heal	Luke	her

Teachers' note As a group exercise, children could sort the cards into columns for **ea** and **oo** and **er** sounds. They could then play snap to reinforce the sounds. You may need to consider regional accents when doing this work.

Developing Literacy Year 2 © A & C Black 1998

Lost vowels

- **Write the missing vowels.**
- **Read the names of the animals.**

p __ nd __

h __ n

r __ bb __ t

__ l __ ph __ nt

f __ sh

fr __ g

sn __ k __

d __ ck

- **Write the names of other animals, with spaces for the vowels.**
- **Ask a partner to write in the vowels.**

Teachers' note The children could write their names and those of others in the class, omitting the vowels, for a partner to complete.

Developing Literacy Year 2
© A & C Black 1998

Making new words

- Add one of the letters to make a new word.
- Read the new word.

cane

c r ane

fat

f __ at

bad

ba __ d

let

le __ t

log

lo __ g

hip

__ hip

Now try this!

- Write some other words to which you can add a letter.
- Write the new words you can make.

Teachers' note The children could write words on squared paper, with each letter in its own square. They mask one square and ask a partner what letter is missing. The partner could ask for clues as to the meaning of the word.

Developing Literacy Year 2
© A & C Black 1998

ck and nk endings

- **Write the words you can make.**
- **Read the words.**

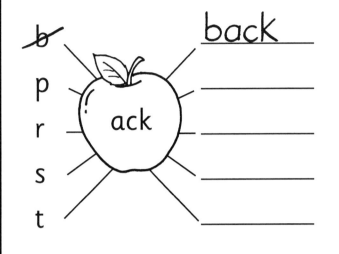

~~b~~   back

p

r   **ack**

s

t

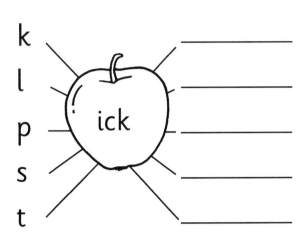

k

l

p   **ick**

s

t

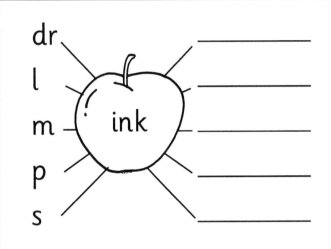

dr

l

m   **ink**

p

s

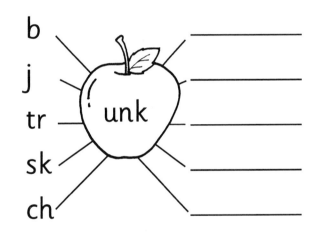

b

j

tr   **unk**

sk

ch

Now try this!

- **Write some more words with these endings.**

$\boxed{ck}$ $\boxed{nk}$

_____   _____

_____   _____

_____   _____

_____   _____

Teachers' note Some children might be able to think of and write words which have **ck** or **nk** in the middle, for example, ticket, racket, pickle, pocket. Others could look for them in books.

Developing Literacy Year 2
© A & C Black 1998

47

- **Use this word circle to make words which end in ll.**

- **Write them on the word circle.**

- **Read the words you have made.**

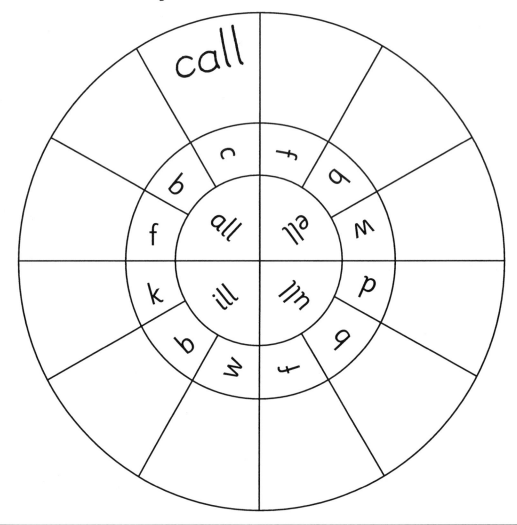

- **Write other words which have these endings.**

| all | ell | ill | ull |

_____   _____   _____   _____

_____   _____   _____   _____

_____   _____   _____   _____

Teachers' note Some children might be able to think of and write words which have **ll** in the middle, for example, yellow, follow, silly, balloon. Others could look for them in books.

Developing Literacy Year 2
© A & C Black 1998

Word wheels

- **Work with a partner.**
- **Cut out the circles.**
- **Put the small circle in the middle of the big circle.**
- **Put a paper fastener through the middle.**
- **Take turns to rotate the big circle to make real words.**

You need a paper fastener.

fluff

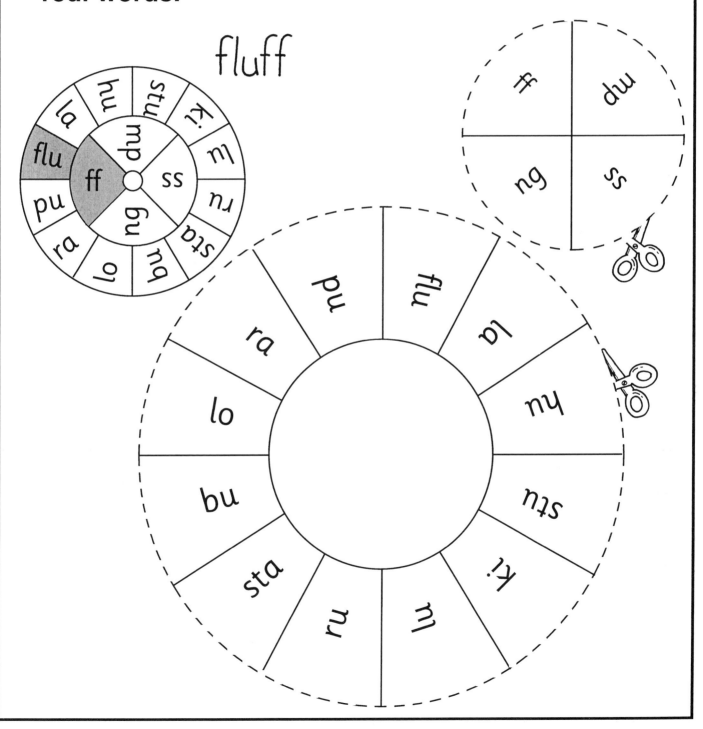

Teachers' note Ask the children to list the words they make and to read them aloud. Are they real words? They could cross out those which are not.

Developing Literacy Year 2
© A & C Black 1998

49

Word tangle

- **Follow the lines.**
- **Read the words.**
- **Write the words.**

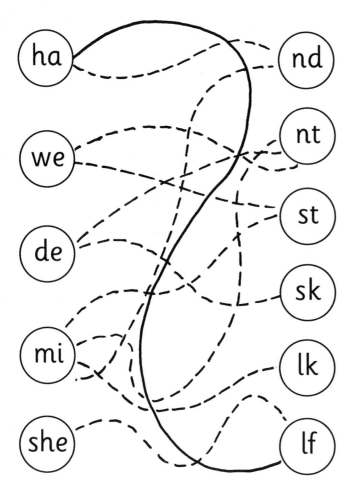

Words

half

_____

_____

_____

_____

_____

_____

_____

_____

_____

Now try this!

- **Write other words with these endings.**

| nd | nt | st | sk | lk | lf |

_____ _____ _____

_____ _____ _____

_____ _____ _____

Teachers' note For more practice mask beginnings and endings and replace with those of your own choice. You may have to add or mask some of the dotted lines.

Developing Literacy Year 2
© A & C Black 1998

Subtraction word puzzles

- **Read the word.**
- **Copy it.**
- **Cover one letter with a counter to make a new word.**
- **Write the new word.**

You need a counter or button.

crab

cab

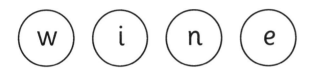

_____

→ _____

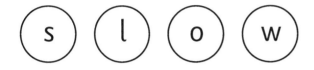

_____

→ _____

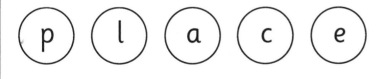

_____

→ _____

_____

→ _____

Now try this

- **Make up some subtraction word puzzles of your own.**

Teachers' note To provide more practice before children do the extension activity, make a second copy of the page masking the letters of the words and replace them with others of your choice, for example, shed, chip, steam and train.

Developing Literacy Year 2
© A & C Black 1998

Word dominoes

- **Work with a partner.**
- **Glue the page on to card.**
- **Cut out the dominoes.**
- **Take turns to put a domino on the table.**

Make a line of dominoes. Touching dominoes must make a real word.

| ish | s | ack | l | ine | t | ime | c |

ime	c

ine	t

eat	w

ake	d

b

ong	n

ean	r

ub

ack	l

g
ile

h
low

m
ive

ish	s

ate	p

ose	f

Teachers' note By supplying the children with a long line of empty domino shapes, some children might be able to make and use their own word dominoes. Alternatively, replace the letters with those of your own choice.

Developing Literacy Year 2
© A & C Black 1998

Word chain

- Write your own words on these word chains.

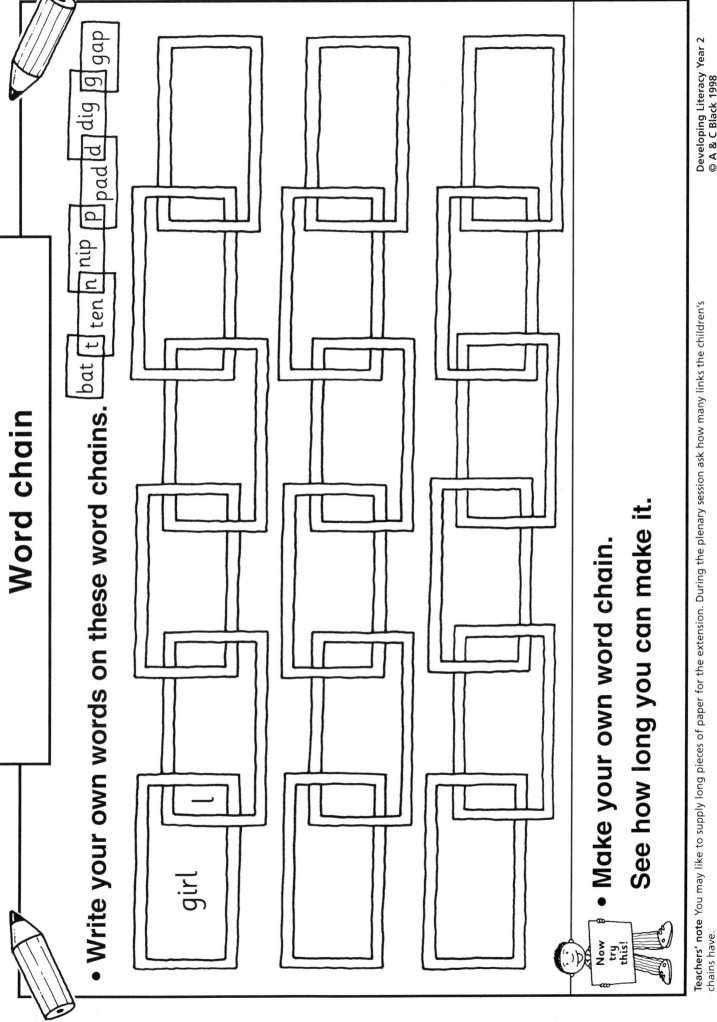

bat | t | ten | n | nip | p | pad | d | dig | g | gap

girl | l

- Make your own word chain.
- See how long you can make it.

Now try this!

Teachers' note You may like to supply long pieces of paper for the extension. During the plenary session ask how many links the children's chains have.

Developing Literacy Year 2
© A & C Black 1998

Word link

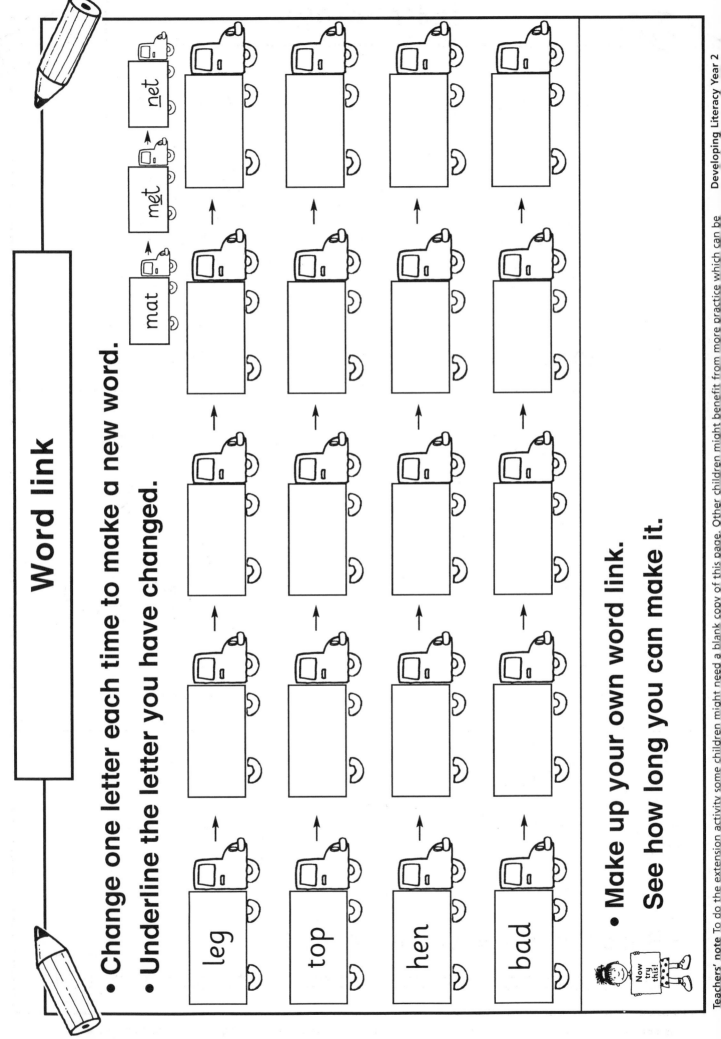

- Change one letter each time to make a new word.
- Underline the letter you have changed.

mat → m<u>e</u>t → <u>n</u>et

leg →

top →

hen →

bad →

- Make up your own word link.
  See how long you can make it.

Now try this!

Teachers' note To do the extension activity some children might need a blank copy of this page. Other children might benefit from more practice which can be   Developing Literacy Year 2

ed endings

walk + | ed |

Natalia _____ to school.

wait + | ed |

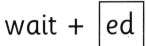

We _____ for a bus.

bump + | ed |

Dad _____ the car.

pick + | ed |

Ryan _____ some flowers.

Now try this!

- **Add** | ed | **to these words.**

watch _____

jump _____

post _____

want _____

- **Read the words you have made.**

- **List some other words to which you can add** | ed | **.**

Teachers' note During the plenary session, give the children some examples, in sentences, of adding
ed which are wrong, for example, gived, goed and bringed. Can the children correct them?

Developing Literacy Year 2
© A & C Black 1998

on large sheet

eat + ing

Raymond is _____ rice.

drink + ing

Meera is _____ juice.

read + ing

James is _____ a story.

walk + ing

Emma is _____ her dog.

• **Write** ing **words in the spaces.**

We were p _____ football.

Mum was p _____ flowers.

Dad was w _____ the car.

• **Write your own sentences using** ing **words made from these words.**

send   look   go

Teachers' note The children could look in books for examples of **ing** words. They could begin an **ing** word bank.

Developing Literacy Year 2
© A & C Black 1998

Using ing words

I open the door.
I am _____ the door.

Tom jumps.
Tom is _____ .

We rolled up the mat.
We were _____
up the mat.

He posted a letter.
He was _____
a letter.

Now try this!

- **Look for** ing **words in books.**
- **List six** ing **words which you find.**

Teachers' note Words have been chosen where it is not neccessary to remove any letters before adding **ing**.

Developing Literacy Year 2
© A & C Black 1998

Plurals

- **Read the words on the notepad.**
- **Add** ⬚s⬚ **or** ⬚es⬚ **to make each word into its plural.**
- **Write the words in the correct set.**

s	**es**
bags	boxes

Notepad words:
- b̶o̶x̶
- b̶a̶g̶
- match
- shoe
- bush
- crash
- car
- fax
- dress
- shirt
- flex
- pass
- slope
- harness
- patch

Now try this!

- **With a partner, write a rule which will help you remember when a plural needs** ⬚es⬚ **.**

Teachers' note The children should notice that words ending in **sh, ch, x** and double consonants need **es** for their plurals.

Developing Literacy Year 2
© A & C Black 1998

Words ending ful

- **Complete the labels with words ending** ful **.**

care

Look for the clues in the thought bubbles.

a _____ driver

a _____ doze

peace

play

a _____ kitten

grace

a _____ swan

Now try this!

- **List five more words to which you can add** ful **.**
- **Write the new words you can make.**

Teachers' note Some children might be able to make up their own **ful** words, by adding **ful** to words such as fright and power. You could also give words like bright and slow and ask the children to recognise the words which are wrong.

Developing Literacy Year 2
© A & C Black 1998

Name puzzles

p
a
t

Pat

Now try this!

- **Write your name.**
- **Draw a picture for each letter.**
- **Make some more name puzzles.**

Teachers' note The children change the first letter of each name to a capital. Displays could be made by groups of children who could cut out and glue on to sugar paper, pictures whose first letters spell their names or those of others in the class.

Developing Literacy Year 2
© A & C Black 1998

Words from names

- **Cut out the letters.**

J   a   m   e   s

- **Make some words from James.**
- **List the words you have made.**

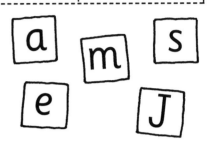

Name	Words
James	as,

- **Make some words from your name and your friends' names.**
- **List the words you have made.**

Name	Words

Teachers' note During the extension, some children may like to use plastic or wooden letters to help them.

Developing Literacy Year 2
© A & C Black 1998

- **Read the rhyme.**
- **Circle the pairs of rhyming words with the same colour.**

Mary had a little lamb,
Whose fleece was white as snow.
And everywhere that Mary went,
The lamb was sure to go.

It followed her to school one day;
Which was against the rule.
It made the children laugh and play,
To see a lamb at school.

- **Write the words you have circled which rhyme with** toe , pool **and** spray .

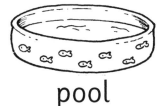

toe   pool   spray

_____   _____   _____

_____   _____   _____

Now try this!

- **List some more words which rhyme with** toe, pool **and** spray .

toe   pool   spray

_____   _____   _____

_____   _____   _____

_____   _____   _____

Teachers' note Ask the children to copy a short rhyme from a book and to circle in the same colour the words which rhyme.

Developing Literacy Year 2
© A & C Black 1998

Colour rhymes

a <u>red</u> bed

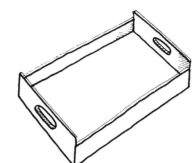

a _____ tray

a _____ shoe

a _____ drink

a _____ sack

a _____

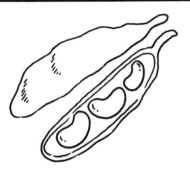

a _____ bean

a _____ _____

a _____ _____

Now try this!

- **Make up your own colour rhymes.**
- **These words may help.**

sink   glue   crown   day

Teachers note The children could give rhyming clues for the colours, for example, 'It rhymes with **think**', and ask a partner which colour they are thinking of. Other rhymes than those given on the page include said, bread (red); hay, pay (grey); moo, do (blue), and so on.

Developing Literacy Year 2
© A & C Black 1998

Silly rhymes

a __pig__ doing a __jig__

a _____ in _____

a _____ in _____

a _____ in a _____

_____ in a _____

- **Make up some other silly rhymes.**
- **These words may help.**

slug   egg   zip

Teachers' note The children could contribute to a class word bank of rhyming words.

Developing Literacy Year 2
© A & C Black 1998